# Swings and Roundabouts

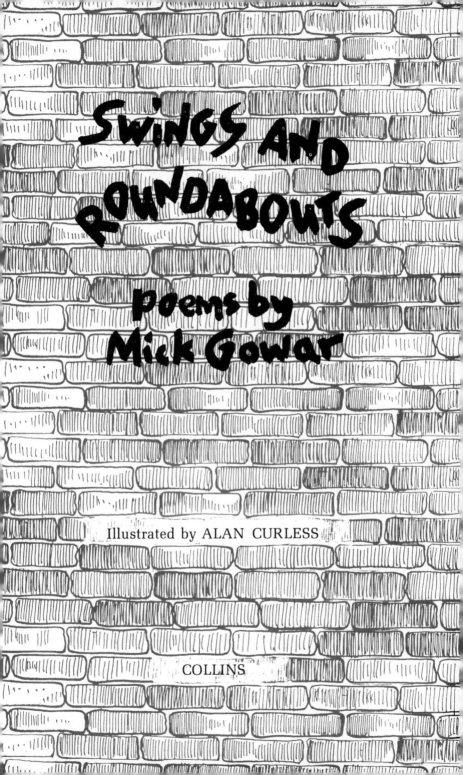

# Swings and Roundabouts

## poems by Mick Gowar

Illustrated by ALAN CURLESS

COLLINS

William Collins Sons & Co Ltd
London · Glasgow · Sydney · Auckland
Toronto · Johannesburg

First published 1981
Second impression 1985
© Mick Gowar 1981
Illustrations © Alan Curless 1981

ISBN 0 00 184527 6 (hardback)
ISBN 0 00 184531 4 (paperback)

Printed and Bound in Great Britain by
Butler & Tanner Ltd, Frome and London

# Contents

## Pioneer

Who needs jungles for excitement
Climbing mountains fording streams
Risking life and limb in London's
Quite enough for me

Pebble dash to scrape your elbows
Paving slabs to graze your knees
Kerbs and gutters turn your ankles
Quite enough for me

Trucks that thunder down the street
The car that never seems to see
A cyclist or a zebra crossing's
Quite enough for me

And in the park there's stinging nettles
Clawing roses file-barked trees
Dogs and what they leave behind it's
Quite enough for me

And vicious beasts I've got as well
A cat that spits and brings in fleas
With spiders prowling round the bath that's
Quite enough for me

So keep your tigers sharks piranhas
I'll just stay in Palmers Green
Being bold in our back garden's
Quite enough for me

## Dad's Garden

My Dad's very keen on gardening
but it's
gardening *INDOORS*
My sister tells her friend, "He's one of those
Gardening Bores."
That's a bit strong
but
for just about as long
as I can remember
from January to December
we've had
sacks of potting compost
where the sofa ought to be
we've got flowerpots and tubs
where the saucepans used to be
we're being driven mad as hatters
by sharing the same flat as
The Greatest Urban Farmer
That The World Will Ever See.

Dad's trouble is we're living in
the towers up The Green
but it doesn't stop old Dad from growing
stocks and spuds and beans and
sprouts and broccoli
but what gets really up our noses
is him manuring his roses
in the kitchen
when we're trying to eat our tea.
Yes we've got
sacks of potting compost
where the sofa ought to be
we've got flowerpots and tubs
where the saucepans used to be
we're being driven mad as hatters
by sharing the same flat as
The Greatest Urban Farmer
That The World Will Ever See.

Only Mum can still remember when
Dad was like most other Dads
before he took to Gardening
and he had more normal fads like
playing darts
or a Night School class in Art
(for beginners)
or cooking Chinese dinners.
But I don't like it when I hear Mum
complaining to her friends
and I hear them saying:
"I wouldn't stand for it, tell you that for nothing."
"No, I'd flush his stupid seeds down the lav and
sling those filthy pots down the rubbish chute."
"Yes, Pam, you want to get these ideas out of his head.
Make him behave like any normal sensible man would."

That's why I try to lend a hand to
my Dad when I can
and we stack
sacks of potting compost
where the sofa ought to be
we pile
flowerpots and tubs
where the saucepans used to be
And it really doesn't matter
I could do worse than share the flat of
The Greatest Urban Farmer
That The World Will Ever See.

## Cat

He hasn't got a name
the cat who owns me
doesn't need one
he knows who's boss around here
O.K.
He's a street cat
cool and loving
to lie out in all the warmest spots
he knows the lot
the cat who owns me

The cat who owns me
hasn't always lived with me
he used to run Mary's place
down the road
but doesn't show his face there
since Mary's baby brother came
he likes his peace and quiet
does the cat who owns me

The cat who owns me
loves to snuggle
down in the daffodils
over the road
Spring cat
and in Summer
the bubbling tarmac or
the top of the dustbin shed
roofed in felt
rolling in the peonies
the cat who owns me

And in Winter time
hurtling through the door
with radiators on the brain
only just remembers to
stick up his tail to say
Hi
toasts himself until
his fur singes
then
far too hot is
frantic to get out again

The cat who owns me
likes to be complimented
on his manners
when eating
I sit on the edge
of the Evening News
he keeps
his food bowls on
and say Good Boy
when he stops
turns his head and
looks
at me then carries on
to his milk and biscuits
very pleased
with himself

But I know the cat who owns me
likes me
really
because he comes to sleep
on my chest
when I'm ill in bed
or lying on the sofa
in an eiderdown
getting better

on a sleepy Winter afternoon
when the rain and cold are
shut outside

my cat and I

**Suzy** *Part 1*

My sister Suzy's
always in the loo, see
it's all in with the bathroom
tub and all
but the thing that hurts much more
as I hop outside the door
is knowing
all she's doing
is
fixing up her eyes
or reddening her cheeks
or painting out her chin
or making up
or making down
or some daft thing
and with the thickness of the stuff
it takes her hours to get it off
and twice as long as that to
get it on
again

## Haringey Sunday

A sunlit evening in Pemberton Road

mud spattered chrome being buffed
till it sparkles
Sunday soaped bonnets
gorgeously rainbowed
then sluished hosed and chamoised

cats settle back on the sunny
grimy side of the street
for a bonus nap before dinner

and a slow procession of women in black
carrying vegetables colanders knives
and each with a dining room chair
makes its way up the road

They stop
at the concreted all-in-one
drive lawn path garden where
the oldest black serge skirted
woman sits

an iron pot of peas in her lap
her hands and her short bladed knife
waiting
till everyone sits
in the places of custom

the oldest close to her
the youngest must sit
till the years bring them in
on the pavement
constantly moving to
let through their children
with bats and balls
a man with a bucket and sponge

They sit and they peel and they talk
and they talk
the oldest with hands moving deft and unwatched
unnoticed unneeded the light slowly dims
soon they will go

to complete their meals with
a bowl of fresh peas
or string beans
but not yet

just one more word
for their white peeling houses
under a sun like a furnace
for their earth red with iron
for their vines and their olives
for their husbands and sons

just one more word

until

        tomorrow

## Fat Boy

I know it
I know it
You don't have to tell me
shouting it out for the whole world to hear
I know it
I know it
I'm fat and
I know it
So there's no need to call out
those dreary old names

like Hippo
or Blubber Guts
Whale Meat Again
I know what I am
I don't have to be told
Never picked out for football
it's always – "You have him"
always the last one
and always in goal

I'm trying
I'm trying
but it's so hard to diet
at home they just tease me
and pile up my plate
"He's watching his figure
he must have a girlfriend"
But I don't even know
how to ask for a date

How could I
at my size they don't even notice
so what if they did?
they'd be forced to say No

All the world loves
a nice jolly fat Friar Tuck?
You can take that old cliche
and stuff it

*I know*

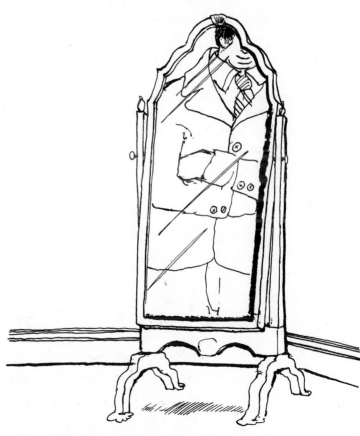

## Ducklings

Here I am the stranger
foreign in a foreign land
standing in a sun-cracked red dirt yard
back home for Mum and Dad
a thousand miles from home for me

The landscape like a mixed up dream
the farm perched high above
deep bitten valleys and
in a distant circle limestone cliffs
a hundred miles from sea

And here I am
feeding Uncle's ducklings
who gobble gobble gobble
every scrap of corn I throw them
scrambling over hard baked cart ruts
climbing over fallen brothers
rushing headlong to get
big and fat

just how Uncle wants them
Laughing from the doorway
behind – the flagstoned kitchen
shuttered cool and dark

a glass of wine held out to me
everybody's waiting and
I've been forgiven

my soft and stupid yesterday
Poor little English
too tender of the heart to eat
the slab of coarse fat
duck's liver pâté
home made

for the foreigner
so foolish rude and clumsy
standing in a red dirt yard
a thousand miles from home

## Pull for Gran

Goodness gracious what a scramble
Granny's hand's caught in the mangle
Mum says, "Serves you right you know
when you get out then out it goes."

So butter on
and hang on tight
and pull for Gran
with all your might

Oh my goodness what a hubub
Gran's got caught up in the twin-tub
smart and new that Mum just bought her
Gran says, "Knew you shouldn't ought to
buy that posh new fangled thing
I was happier mangling."

So twist the dials
and hang on tight
and pull for Gran
with all your might

Goodness gracious what a drama
Gran's got stuck in the launderama
she didn't want the public gaze
on age old whites that now are greys
so to avoid it slipped the catch
slammed the door and bust the latch.
Says, "I wouldn't be in this tangle
if you'd let me keep my mangle."

So grab the handle
hang on tight
and pull for Gran
with all your might

So now Mum does all Granny's washing
and moans around like something shocking
complains about the work involved
while Gran just sits there growing old
and sometimes thinks, I shouldn't wonder,
of mangling days when she was younger
when she would have to wash for Mum
when Mum was helpless, small, and young

So all join hands
and hold on tight
and pull for Gran
with all your might

**Suzy** *Part 2*

My sister Sue is
still there in the loo
and it's getting worse and worse
I'm sure to burst
and though if Dad has told her once
he must have said a thousand times
she still thinks she's
the only one that counts
And her precious heated rollers
and her layers of mascara
and her eyebrows
and her earholes
and the rest

is the only thing that matters
and she still ignores the batters
on the door
as the rest of us go
MAD

## Grymsdyke

It's down
demolished now
the house that stood
out beyond the shops beyond the school

Strictly Out Of Bounds

the house with locked iron gates
and all the fences beaten flat
where we used to charge
the wagon trains or sword fight
round the gate top eagles we'd
killed with bricks the week before

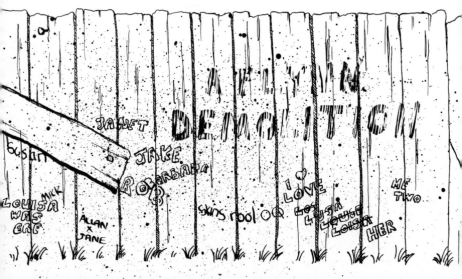

Four storeys high and
every window shattered
but the walls were solid cover for
we commandoes – silent killers
hiding round the corner

Or on the far side of the house
All-In Pom Pom One Two Three
against the girth of the giant
tree whose bottom branches
loaded down by their immenseness
scarred the ground and
gave us springboards for
leaping on a passing horseman

And there
behind the house
fifty yards beyond the dead
bare dirt circle
beneath the twilight of the tree –
an ornamental lake hung
clogged and scummy
where once a man had drowned
for real
in just four feet of water
and never broke the surface
A famous man who
one hot summer day
left house and croquet lawns and tea
and never made it to the surface
caught in weed
somewhere around the middle

It never bothered us
we'd talked about it
all agreed if he'd stood up
he could have lived
then one bright summer day
in the garden
snared by creepers
I was run away from
discarded for my clumsiness


Left to hide and seek alone
I passed the darkness of the tree
to find the lake in sunlight
and I saw the bubbles
of his screams
fluttering

the weed
choked
surface
somewhere
around
the middle

## Skipping Game

Kick a can against the wall
Sus Sus
You don't bother me at all
Sus Sus
Walking down the busy street
Sus Sus
Jive Talk Dread Locks Tapping Feet
Sus Sus
Head High Mind High Walking Proud
Sus Sus
Lots of Backchat Laughing Loud
Sus Sus
Standing waiting for a bus
Sus Sus
Just standing waiting for a bus
Sus Sus

Just
Standing
Waiting
Sus

## Half Term

Up and down
Up and down
the lift's all there is on a rainy day
Up and down
Up and down
the stair's all there is on a rainy day
And nobody likes it
least of all us
but what can you do
on a rainy day

Right down there
off Fulberry Road
on that long strip of grass
that nobody uses
Jeffrey and Me and Wayne and Jim
We Are The Champions !! ! !!
Champions of Europe !! ! !!
And you should hear the roars
from the millions of fans
at the Empty House End
as I slide in a penalty
just on the whistle
Easy Easy Easy
But up here through the rain
and the grey clinging cloud
you can peer till your head aches
it's all disappeared

Up and down
Up and down
the lift's all there is on a rainy day
Up and down
Up and down
the stair's all there is on a rainy day
And nobody likes it
least of all us
but what can you do
on a rainy day

Swimming with Wayne
that's what I like best
at the Pickett's Lock pool
with cokes in the cafe then
walk round the golf course
looking for balls
Then we sit by the stream
half the way round
selling them back for 10p each
But it's
"Not in this weather
you must be mad
You're not going out
on a day like this"

Up and down
Up and down
the lift's all there is on a rainy day
Up and down
Up and down
the stair's all there is on a rainy day
And nobody likes it
least of all us
but what can you do
on a rainy day

I'm too old for Play School
the horse racing's awful
I've read all the comics
twice through today
Wayne's got a cold
and nobody's coming
we can't have a dog
because of The Rules

Up and down
Up and down
the lift's all there is on a rainy day
Up and down
Up and down
the stair's all there is on a rainy day
Nobody likes it
and since the complaints
there's not even that
on a rainy day

## Remembering St Mary's Churchyard

It took the two of us an hour or more to climb
the grass side of the hill
we stopped and started looped and
ran great circles in what adults thought
a ten minute walk at most

Between the fencing fringe of oaks
a sweep of grass for rolling in or flopping over dead
and up again at "Ten" to fight
a path through Viking bracken
crisp as shredded wheat

Lords of the grassy slopes
all day all week all month we had
as far as we could see was ours
the sun would climb above the station
all day long through perfect blue

We climbed the churchyard gate and walked
into a garden in which time stood still
unrecognisable to us no lawns no concrete paths
no flowers we knew no stunted coloured clusters
but mysterious severe like stick-faced spinsters
dowdy speckled bell-shaped heads
and brittle feathered leaves
plants forgotten for a hundred years
We cut them down
and headed for the bench beneath the western wall
to eat our lunch


But never did
for she sat there
crying
with her hands unmoving in her lap
holding a pad of blank white paper
and a pencil
She never looked at us
She never moved
She never even
brought her hands up to her face
to hide her tears
She didn't care
what we might think of her

the mad girl crying on the bench
Not old    not old like
Crazy Jack who screamed at cars
in St Anne's Road
but old enough to us
[Less than twenty]
in a summer frock
too tight
stretched taut across
a baby growing
big inside her

We knew that bulk
and what it meant
so what was there to cry about?
Why?
with her sketch pad
open untouched
on her lap
Why should she cry
no shame no pride
not trying to stop
or even dry her tears

It didn't seem important
but we walked away as quietly as we could
and in the afternoon
forgot her

### Suzy *Part 3*

Oh thank God
she's out at last
and at last the danger's past
but the thing that left the bathroom
wasn't her
it had thick mud on its face
and its hair was all in snakes
wrapped round curlers
and its fingernails were green
Now the thing that bothers me is
that it took about an hour
for her to look as ugly as
a witch
so how much longer will it take
and how much suffering for me to
turn that monster
back to Suzy
once
again

## History

When I was a lad so young
    I went to school in
    a big grey town called
    Stinky Brum,
When I was a lad so young.


When I was a lad so young
    I went to school in
    a blazer
    that hung
    right down my back
    like a plastic mac,
    in a big grey town called
    Stinky Brum,
When I was a lad so young.


When I was a lad so young
    I went to school in
    galoshes
    that clung
    to my outdoor shoes,

in a blazer that hung
right down my back
like a plastic mac,
in a big grey town called
Stinky Brum,
When I was a lad so young.


When I was a lad so young
I went to school in
a thick red vest
all smeared with Vick
for my wheezy chest,
in galoshes that clung
to my outdoor shoes,
in a blazer that hung
right down my back
like a plastic mac,
in a big grey town called
Stinky Brum,
When I was a lad so young.


When I was a lad so young
I went to school in
a big brown room
that was filled with
noise and
girls and boys,

in a thick red vest
all smeared with Vick
for my wheezy chest,


in galoshes that clung
to my outdoor shoes,
in a blazer that hung
right down my back
like a plastic mac,
in a big grey town called
Stinky Brum,
When I was a lad so young —

and the smallest thing
in the whole wide world was
                me.

## Moving In

A noisy street?
Yes, it was a noisy street
when we first arrived
and on the first night
I had to share a bed
with Geoff my brother
we couldn't find the other box of sheets
I didn't sleep at all

The trains over back
and the big vans echoing
echoing echoing
I thought I'd never sleep again
A cat cried
just like a baby
over and over again and
something knocked a dustbin over
Geoff so fast asleep
I've never felt so lonely

But in a week or so
your ears shut off
or else they get to like it
You'll see
it's not so bad
You'll get to know it all
just like your old place
near enough

## Rain

Flying in the blue ice of the sky
a pearl in the winds
of the high places

Falling through air
mile after mile to the ground
a mile a minute
a mile a second
to hit the roof and
have to carry on
worming from slate to slate
a hundred droplets years one
brick at a time then
slowly
so slowly
down the window
till halfway in a sudden rush swept down and lost
in the rainlake on the sill

My cheek against the warm
pink candlewick
bedspread
Watching
Waiting
for a sound
just one sound
to say I'm sorry, Mum, I'm sorry
My voice echoes back
"I hate you, I hate you"

Upstairs
wishing wishing
I could walk through a door
into a living room where
it never happened
and start again

## First Boyfriend

Every wheel you can hear
on George V Avenue
can stop your heart dead
but none of them slow
make the turn by the holly tree

One car
only one car
in the whole world
rushing past
time and again and again

He's not coming
Oh God    He's not coming
His Dad won't get the car out
not in this weather

Shush

But don't look
out of the window
or the car won't start
don't look
just listen
to the wet road

Come
Oh Come
Just come
Nothing else
You don't even have to
talk to me
Only come and I'll

Love You
Forever

## Greek Cafe

It's only from the very top of the bus
I can see above the shop front of
plain whitewashed glass

only from here can I look through
two secret forgotten windows
into the place where the men go

Kyrenia painted in big red greek letters
coming home from school I see it
day after day passing

the smoky yellow light hangs
in the rain and rush of
a North London night

Passing the men sipping their coffee
from tiny tiny cups then
water from a bottle

from the traffic seeing
the stubble chinned pool players
caught in mid shot like a photograph

Should the woman next to me
turn her head away
interested and English

is it funny silly make her angry?
must I tell her not to look? that
this is where the men go

## Pictures in the Pillow

I remembered today
so clearly
         so clearly
a child that was me far away
in his mother's bed

woken at night by a sound
or a picture in sleep
that only the warmth of
the big bed could comfort

awake in the dawn
who would gaze
at the blue lantern star
of the paraffin stove
high on the ceiling

and could conjure up pictures

quite simply
I would press my face down
with eyes screwed up tight
deep down in the pillow
and there they would be
falling through darkness like water

A tree

always the first
was a tree
so black
with a black sky behind
and birds
that would flicker and fade

then would come colours
A red making starfish
that whirled
in a sea of white spirals
and sank
into blue

Then was the time

And then was the time
if I pressed
with my hands on my eyes
I could bring
out
the creatures of Night
the
Strange Ones I
couldn't control

They had faces
with rippling smiles
like people
till their eyes disappeared

and the lips became teeth
and their mouths opened wide
and inside was a huge crimson eye
full of hate
that
ever
so
slowly
was
turning
towards    me

I stop
       NOW

and cling to the bedroom
to the sight of the lump ugly dresser
and gravy brown cupboard
and bright yellow curtains

I've seen them
I've seen them and still got away

And the world would come back
only
later I'd
try to imagine
what would happen
                    if

older
and bigger
and stronger I'd
dare to look on

## The Boys in the Market

Davy and me
up here on the eighth
Balmoral House.
Bed.
very quiet
dark
late
but
underneath
the noises have begun
Davy says The Hairies
are down in the market

underneath
down the bed
can still hear them
laughing, the shouting
climbing the stairs
the cowboy yells
the clang of metal frames
The Hairies are out
Davy says

down between the blocks
in front of the shuttered shops
even with the lights on
climbing the stalls
swinging on the poles
bashing on the walls
doors

up on the eighth
here even deep deep down in bed
with my ears
shut
tight as
a bottle
The Hairies are leaping about
shouting,
The Hairies Are Out!

## Launderette

We share the humping of the bags
and mine it weighs a ton up the road and
and and round the corner through
the door into the fish tank glare my
brother Pete's come home again but
just for the weekend and
We put them down

He grins and shakes his hands
down around his knees like a gorilla
hands as limp as gloves
hands like mine with
wide stripes going red
from the thick white plastic handles

It's different here this time
at night
dustier and so much glass
the washers and the dryers
throwing back your face with blown out cheeks
and no head
and the plastic wood on the back wall
slimy with light
And men with beards and jeans
All men

We load the washing in
Three machines full up
he's got everything
like us but
just for him
sheets and tablecloths
even pillowcases
And two thick check shirts
and a pair of green jeans
I've never seen before

We sit down on the bench
Pete crosses his arms across his chest
and leans back
so do I
He gives me a stick of chewing gum
and a wink
just like

a
   friend

## Dinner Party Blues

I eat

Children's food
and I hate it
You know the old rubbish I mean
dead worms in red puke called spaghetti
and always the good old baked beans

My parents are giving a party tonight
Just a few people coming to "dine"
And everyone's stomach gets filled with delights
With just one exception — that's mine

I got

Children's food
and I hate it
two hours before they arrived
not cheese but
wet rubber all wrapped up in foil
and toast that was burnt on both sides

At six-thirty tonight I was tortured
Though Mum never noticed my plight
When I sat in the kitchen and ate my baked beans
While she cooked a roast duck for tonight

I had

Children's food
and I hate it
beefburgers instead of real meat
and never whole fish
just the fingers
all the bits that the grown ups won't eat

Oh why can't they feed us like adults
Oh why can't I stay up till late
And eat all the things I can smell here upstairs
Instead of the kid's stuff I hate

But it's

Children's food
and I loathe it
You know the old rubbish I mean
it's anything frozen or
out of a tin
or anything served with baked beans

## Tower Block Net Curtains

The blank chapped topless face of
concrete in the wind the rain the cloud
not brown not grey
the drab cold heart of both
Stark
You can't argue back
to the tower block flats

But don't turn your back
walk away
Wait

Look

The windows are
coming alive

Look

Some fairly plain
straight and unfussed
just what you'd expect
fishing nets and chicken wire
pin cushion prickings and spiders' webs
But some
you look twice and
you still don't believe

There's a pair
just up there
made from two frilly knickers
with billowing legs
that reach to the sill
and next door
huge and full and
held back by ribbons
a bosomy fat-bummed
Lady of Lace

Or there
on the fourth
a Compendium Box
of all different games —
a chessboard next door to
noughts and crosses with
snakes and ladders
two floors below

The trimmings of borders
mount a parade
of military sleeves
a full colonel of
The Ruritanian Rifles
and (slightly shamefaced)
a Kitchen Corporal
line up in neighbouring windows

And
of course
flowers galore
Woven in
or made from the frills
as big and as boastful
as plastic chrysanths

All together
a waterfall
of proud whites
through slightly yellows
to downright greys

And behind and inside
unseen but still watching
The People
who look down at us
looking in
and put up their curtains
to stop
and amaze us

## November 3rd

A rocket with its stick
jammed into the ground
snatched from the box
when no one was looking

into the garden under my coat
rammed in the earth
when all the backs were turned

Ignition
firing into mud
Stuck fast

Just a couple of sparklers
Mark's Dad had said
as a treat before Guy Fawkes

Now spluttering with rage
        speechless moment then
louder and louder – bellowing

his fury at us
rising higher and higher
"Spoiling everything   Everything
Just never enough Never satisfied"

His words like whipping twigs
that sting hot tears
too much shame to hear him
on and on

of how we would have had
some hot tomato soup
and all been happy

not now   No
You two put an end to that
now everyone must do without

Because of us
no treats
no happiness

through all the tears
a blackened twisted wreck
of burned out wood and paper
crushed beneath my boot

## Daddy

Daddy lives in Tate Street now
he's got a flat
with patchy orange walls
and grey armchairs that
smell of someone else
And every Saturday we sleep there
Jo and me

Daddy lives in Tate Street now
he's got a flat
it's up a winding flight of stairs
it's cold and
dark at night it feels as though there's
no one there
not even Daddy Jo and me

Daddy lives in Tate Street now
he's got a flat
he grows tomatoes in a pot outside
and in a week or two
we'll help him put them on
a windowsill to ripen
Daddy says

Daddy lives in Tate Street now
he's got a flat
and we go out a lot
to films and fairs and
Christmas time he'll take us to
A Pantomime
he's Promised

Daddy lives in Tate Street now
he's got a flat
he takes us home on Sunday
Mummy's in the kitchen  Dick's there too
he's cooking something
Daddy says Goodbye
                         and then
goes home

## Coming Home

It's not really scary
when you come in the house
and nobody's there

        it's just

that the chairs seem to
stare
and the room looks so big and
the deep sounds of quiet
make a buzz in your ears

        and

Mum'll be back soon
it's really all right
the teapot's all ready
I'm not at all frightened
I'll switch on the TV
but not for a minute

I'll just sit here
I don't want to move from the chair
and it's not really scary
I'm not at all frightened
and only a *Baby* would start to believe
that something invisible's
sitting behind

I'll look in a minute
Yes, that's what I'll do
in a minute I'll look

I'll just sit here
and soon I'll switch on
the TV
in a minute or two
it's only a box – after all
just a box and I know that
it can't really whisper
those horrible things
when it isn't switched on

                              cos

I'm old enough now
Yes, I'm old enough now and
I don't really mind
No, I don't really mind
cos

   it's only till Six

## Would You Believe It

– Jacky's going out with Peter –
– Which one? NOT the one with spots –
– No of course not, Peter DAVIS –
– Don't believe you
                              how d'you know? –
– Tracy told me but you mustn't say
I said so –
                    – course not
how did she find out? –
– Well,
Phillipa, that's Tracy's mate the one in 3G
her mate Mandy's sister Carol's
best friend Susan and her boyfriend
(his name's Peter)
saw them
                    Coming Out The Pictures

(But you mustn't tell A SOUL
'cos Jacky's also going out
with someone else as well . . .

## My Dog Old Yellow

Once I had a sausage dog
Twice he caught a Ginger Tom who
Three times round the garden chased him
Four long scratches quite disgraced him

Made dog turn the tale and run
Proud dogs never have much fun

## Christmas Thank You's

Dear Auntie
Oh, what a nice jumper
I've always adored powder blue
and fancy you thinking of
orange and pink
for the stripes
how clever of you!

Dear Uncle
The soap is
terrific
So
useful
and such a kind thought and
how did you guess that
I'd just used the last of
the soap that last Christmas brought

Dear Gran
Many thanks for the hankies
Now I really can't wait for the flu
and the daisies embroidered
in red round the "M"
for Michael
how
thoughtful of you!

Dear Cousin
What socks!
and the same sort you wear
so you must be
the last word in style
and I'm certain you're right that the
luminous green
*will* make me stand out a mile

Dear Sister
I quite understand your concern
it's a risk sending jam in the post
But I think I've pulled out
all the big bits
of glass
so it won't taste too sharp
spread on toast

Dear Grandad
Don't fret
I'm delighted
So *don't* think your gift will
offend
I'm not at all hurt
that you gave up this year
and just sent me
a fiver
to spend

## Alnmouth Beach

Alnmouth grey is
sky and sea that
merge out where the big ships disappear

a drizzle clinging to the blades
of rasp tongued grass
a mist that breathes across the dead end sand

Alnmouth grey is
concrete blocks to
halt the tanks that never land

standing like a giant row of
serpents' teeth to dare the winter gales
to try again to wash away

But she can
mask it well
this beach – with Alnmouth blue

when sea and golden sand compete
like beauty queens
beneath a sky pond so secure

This Alnmouth blue
confection strewn with
sticky sugar spun in threads of cloud

as cosy and as homely as
the reassurance of
discarded wrappers measuring the gentle wind

She has no bite today
you see
she tempts us from our caravans and cars

not caring for our blind discarding:
clotted tar will never stick to her
the bottles never pierce her skin

For she is change
Tomorrow or the next day Alnmouth black
obliterates and terrifies the memory as

wave upon wave upon wave upon wave
crashes down on to the beach
and sucks it flat

## One for the Road

Here's one for the road and
two for the cul-de-sac
three for the avenue
four for the drive
five for the crescent
and
SIXTY for my street
that's the number I live at
we're there now

Good-bye